BOOK THREE

How racism came to Britain

THE INSTITUTE OF RACE RELATIONS
2-6 Leeke Street, London WC1X 9HS, England

Cartoons drawn by Christine Smith
Text and storyline by the Institute of Race Relations

© Institute of Race Relations 1985
   ISBN 0 85001 029 2

Typesetting by Lithoprint Ltd (TU), 28 Shacklewell Lane, London E8
Printed by the Russell Press (TU), Gamble Street, Nottingham
Published and distributed by the Institute of Race Relations

Contents

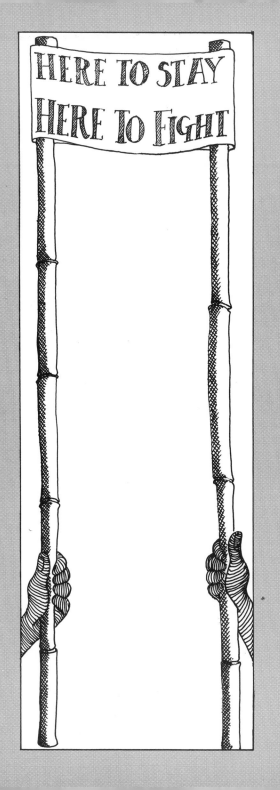

Preface

This is a sequel to the two Anti-racist Educational Books for Young People, *Roots of racism* and *Patterns of racism*, which we brought out at the time that the Rampton (subsequently Swann) Committee on the educational needs of 'ethnic minorities' was sitting.

There we pointed out that the development and promotion of multicultural education did nothing to tackle the fundamental issue of racism. For, 'while multicultural studies may, in explaining differences in customs and culture, help to modify attitudes, such studies are primarily an extension of existing educational techniques and methods, and, as such, allow racism within society, and within the educational system, to pass unchallenged. And education itself comes to be seen in terms of an adjustment process within a racist society and not as a force for changing the values that make that society racist. Ethnic minorities do not suffer disabilities because of ethnic differences, but because such differences are given differential weightage in a system of racial hierarchy.'

Hence, our concern was not centrally with multicultural, multi-ethnic education but with anti-racist education (which by its very nature would include the study of other cultures). Just to learn about other people's cultures is not to learn about the racism of one's own. To learn about the racism of one's own culture, on the other hand, is to approach other cultures objectively.

Since then, our critique of multiculturalism has been accepted and perverted — not least by the 'anti-racist' educational establishment — to mean not the study of racism in white culture and society but of racist attitudes among white people. The first locates the problem in the power and profit relationships between nations and peoples, the second in the personal relationships between individuals and/or groups.

This book attempts to restore the study of racism to its proper perspective and, in relating British racism to its particular history in slave and colonial oppression and exploitation, make clear its growth and prevalence within British society today. The cartoon format, we hope, will help to take the ideas beyond the classroom and make them accessible to a wider range of readers.

We are indebted to the Greater London Council's Ethnic Minorities Unit for lightening our financial burden in other areas and so letting us get on with our long-term educational work against racism. But, most of all, we owe thanks to our intrepid young cartoonist Christine Smith whose willingness to learn about her country's racism, coupled with her commitment to bring it to book, gives hope for the future.

A. Sivanandan
Director
Institute of Race Relations
June 1985

INTRODUCTION

ASIA
AFRICA
AMERICA

...so, are there any questions?

?

ASIA
AFRICA
AMERICA

Why did black people come to Britain?

To answer that we will have to ask why white people went over to their countries, robbed them of their land and riches, enslaved their people and taught their children to be more loyal to this country than to their own—and justified it all by developing the idea that white people were superior to black people. And then, when we have answered that, you will find that the question is no longer why black people came to Britain, but how racism came to Britain.

So why did white people do all that?

ASIA
AFRICA
AM

Let's go back into the past and find some of the answers...

ONCE UPON A TIME THERE WAS A LAND SURROUNDED BY WATER...

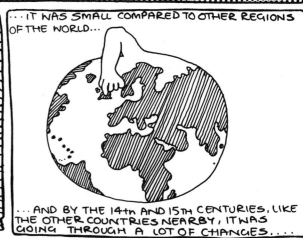

...IT WAS SMALL COMPARED TO OTHER REGIONS OF THE WORLD...

...AND BY THE 14th AND 15th CENTURIES, LIKE THE OTHER COUNTRIES NEARBY, IT WAS GOING THROUGH A LOT OF CHANGES....

At that time <u>everyone</u> from the highest to the lowest in society had to live on what the peasants produced from the land. And what with plagues and warfare, and bad harvests — and the greediness of their lords, there was often not enough to go round. Where did people look for the answers?....

SOME LOOKED TO THE STARS...

BECAUSE THEY THOUGHT THE STARS GOVERNED MEN'S LIVES...

WHILE OTHERS LOOKED TO GOLD....

...OTHER PEOPLE'S GOLD, OF COURSE...

1

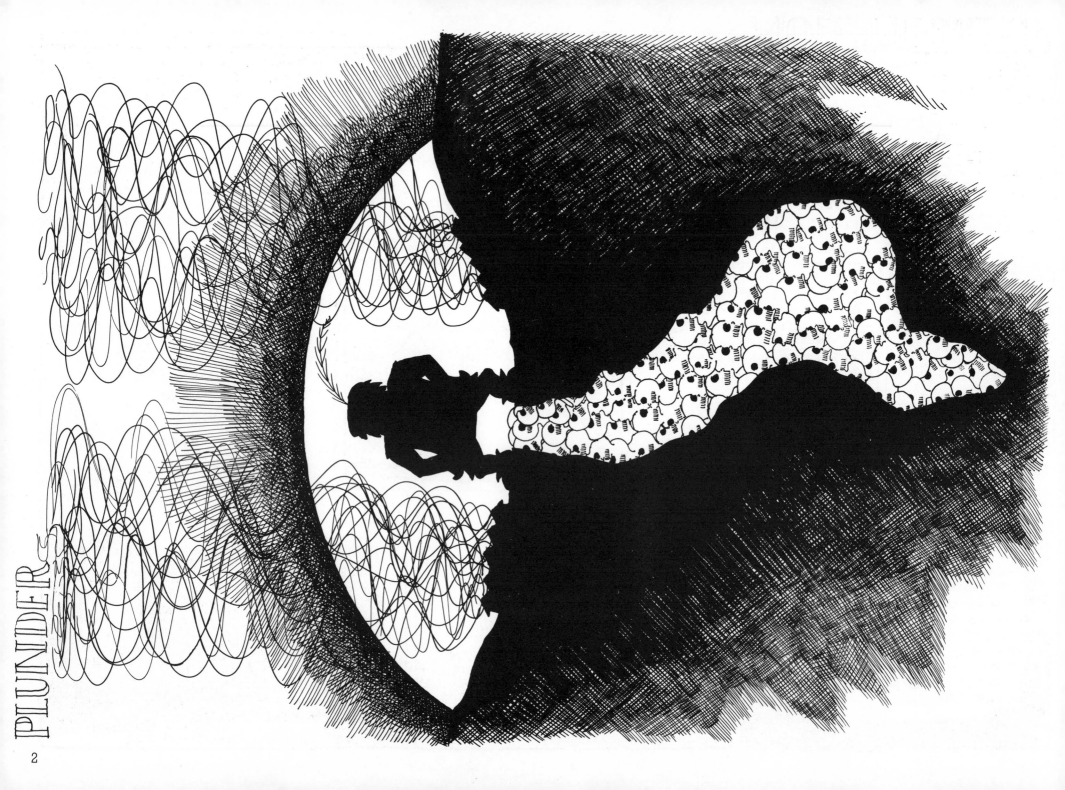

PLUNDER

EXPLORERS BEGAN TO TRAVEL THE WORLD IN SEARCH OF PRECIOUS GOODS TO TRADE IN...

TAKING LUGGAGE ESSENTIAL FOR THEIR PURPOSES...

So, what happened when they got there?...

IN FOURTEEN HUNDRED AND NINETY TWO COLUMBUS SAILED THE OCEAN BLUE...

I think we're about to be discovered!....

THE REGIONS THAT WERE ABOUT TO BE 'DISCOVERED' — THE ISLANDS OF THE CARIBBEAN AND THE MAINLAND OF LATIN AMERICA — WERE WELL ORGANIZED AND HIGHLY DEVELOPED AGRICULTURAL SOCIETIES...

SOCIETIES WHICH PROVIDED FOOD FOR ALL, DEVELOPED THEIR OWN SCIENCES AND RELIGIONS, AND MADE BEAUTIFUL THINGS FROM THE GOLD AND SILVER THEY TOOK FROM THEIR RIVERS AND MOUNTAINS....

3

AT FIRST THE NEWCOMERS WERE TRUSTED AND WELCOMED WITH OPEN ARMS....

Welcome! Help yourself...

BUT WHAT THEY WERE REALLY INTERESTED IN WAS THE GOLD AND SILVER. THEY DID NOT CARE WHAT THEY DID TO GET IT FOR THEMSELVES....

OF COURSE THE PEOPLES ON THE MAINLAND AND ON THE ISLANDS DEFENDED THEMSELVES...

TO JUSTIFY THEIR ACTIONS THE SPANISH AND PORTUGUESE ~ WHO WERE THE FIRST EUROPEAN INVADERS ~ CLAIMED THE PEOPLE WERE SAVAGE AND BARBAROUS, NOT REALLY HUMAN AT ALL...

MOST OF THE PEOPLES OF THE CARIBBEAN ISLANDS WERE WIPED OUT....

BY THE SPANISH, FOLLOWED CLOSELY BY THE ENGLISH WHO WERE NOW QUICK TO GET IN ON THE ACT...

WITHIN A CENTURY THE INVADERS HAD PLUNDERED THE ISLANDS OF THEIR WEALTH....

I'm not going back to England yet! We must be able to get some profit from the land....

THE ENGLISH SET UP PLANTATIONS TO GROW CROPS THEY COULD SELL IN EUROPE...

BUT THERE WEREN'T ENOUGH PEOPLE LEFT ALIVE TO WORK THEM...

Ah.... I know where we can get labour....

AND SO THE ENGLISH SENT SHIPS FROM PORTS SUCH AS BRISTOL, LIVERPOOL, GLASGOW AND LONDON TO AFRICA...

WHERE TEXTILES AND TOOLS WERE EXCHANGED FOR PEOPLE...

...CAUGHT AND BOUGHT AS SLAVES BY THE WHITE TRADERS. THEY WERE FORCED TO LEAVE THEIR OWN LAND TO GO TO THE AMERICAS AND THE CARIBBEAN.

ONCE THE CAPTURED SLAVES ARRIVED...

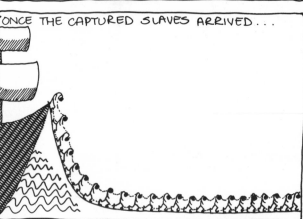

THEY WERE FORCED TO LABOUR ON THE PLANTATIONS TO GROW TOBACCO, SUGAR AND COTTON, WHICH WERE THEN LOADED ON TO THE SHIPS THAT HAD BROUGHT THEM.

THESE SHIPS WOULD THEN SAIL FOR PORTS IN EUROPE SUCH AS BRISTOL, TO SELL THE GOODS ON BOARD.... BRISTOL BECAME STRONG AND WEALTHY THANKS TO THE SLAVE TRADE...

THE WHITES RUNNING THE SLAVE TRADE HAD TO DEVELOP AN ARGUMENT THAT WOULD ALLOW THEM TO BE CHRISTIANS AND SLAVE TRADERS AT THE SAME TIME — DIFFICULT? THEY MANAGED IT...

"A SLAVE IS A THING, A COMMODITY, A PIECE OF PROPERTY — TO BE OWNED, USED, DISPOSED OF. IT HAS NO HISTORY EXCEPT AT ITS POINT OF ENTRY INTO THE MARKET, NO DEFINITION EXCEPT ON A BILL OF SALE."

RICH PLANTATION OWNERS BOUGHT PEOPLE AS SLAVES...

TO BE SOLD AT NEXT MARKET
~
250 FINE HEALTHY NEGRO SLAVES.
JUST ARRIVED FROM WINDWARD ISLES... SUITABLE FOR HARD LABOUR.

AND SINCE THEY WERE COMMODITIES — THINGS TO BE BOUGHT AND SOLD AND THROWN AWAY WHEN DONE WITH — AND NOT HUMANS, THEY HAD NO PLACE BESIDE THE WHITE MAN, ON EARTH OR IN "HEAVEN"...

TRIANGULAR TRADE

THIS SYSTEM OF TRADING — IN WHICH GOODS FROM BRITAIN WERE SOLD FOR SLAVES, THE SLAVES SOLD FOR COTTON AND SUGAR (GROWN BY SLAVES) ON THE PLANTATIONS, AND COTTON AND SUGAR SOLD IN BRITAIN AND MADE INTO THE GOODS THAT WERE TAKEN TO AFRICA TO BE EXCHANGED FOR MORE SLAVES — AMASSED HUGE PROFITS ON EACH TRIP AND WAS CALLED THE TRIANGULAR TRADE. BUT IT'S EASIER TO THINK OF IT AS A CIRCLE ...

" THE PLEASURE, GLORY AND GRANDEUR OF ENGLAND HAS BEEN ADVANCED MORE BY SUGAR THAN BY ANY OTHER COMMODITY."
SIR. D. THOMAS.

IT WAS THE SLAVE AND SUGAR TRADES WHICH MADE BRISTOL THE SECOND CITY OF ENGLAND FOR THE FIRST 75 YEARS OF THE EIGHTEENTH CENTURY...

" THERE IS NOT A BRICK IN THE CITY BUT WHAT IT IS CEMENTED WITH THE BLOOD OF A SLAVE."

C. WHITWORTH. 1781

" IT WAS THE PRICE OF HUMAN FLESH AND BLOOD THAT GAVE US A START IN LIVERPOOL."

SHIP LEAVES EUROPE
1. (FRANCE, SPAIN, HOLLAND AND PORTUGAL INVOLVED TOO)

11. SHIPS LOADED WITH GUNS, TOOLS AND TEXTILES FOR AFRICA, INCLUDING FETTERS AND HANDCUFFS

2. SHIPS SAIL TO AFRICA. (138 SHIPS ARRIVED FROM LIVERPOOL IN 1790)

10. GUNS, TOOLS AND TEXTILES MADE IN INDUSTRIAL REVOLUTION

9. SALE AND PROCESSING OF PRODUCE FUELS INDUSTRIAL REVOLUTION

3. GUNS FROM BIRMINGHAM, TOOLS AND TEXTILES ARE EXCHANGED FOR PEOPLE.

8. SHIP SAILS FOR BRITAIN, AND OTHER EUROPEAN PORTS

4. PEOPLE ARE FORCED TO LEAVE AFRICA. **60** MILLION ARE SOLD AS SLAVES.

7. EMPTY SLAVE SHIP RELOADED WITH SUGAR (TO BRISTOL) AND COTTON (TO MANCHESTER)

6. SLAVES ARE FORCED TO LABOUR ON THE PLANTATIONS.

5. PEOPLE SAIL AS SLAVES TO THE CARIBBEAN, BOUND CLOSELY TOGETHER IN IRON SHACKLES.

7

FOR GENERATIONS PEOPLE WERE BRED INTO SLAVERY.

BUT THEY ALWAYS FOUGHT AGAINST IT IN ANY WAY THEY COULD, ESCAPING TO THE MOUNTAINS,

OR BURNING DOWN THE PLANTATIONS — TILL IT BECAME INCREASINGLY DIFFICULT FOR BRITAIN TO PROFIT FROM SLAVERY AND IT BEGAN TO WITHDRAW....

I think the overheads are getting too expensive here chaps!....

WITHDRAWAL FROM THE CARIBBEAN WAS EXPLAINED DIFFERENTLY IN BRITAIN...

As a Christian I can no longer justify slavery

Besides, there are richer pickings elsewhere..

THE 'ELSEWHERE' WAS INDIA...

o o o

8

WE ARE LOOKING AT INDIA, NOT BECAUSE IT IS THE ONLY EXAMPLE, BUT BECAUSE IT SHOWS UP SOME OF THE DIFFERENT WAYS IN WHICH BRITAIN SYSTEMATICALLY **EXPLOITED** THE LANDS AND LABOUR OF BLACK PEOPLES TO FURNISH ITS OWN DEVELOPMENT INTO AN INDUSTRIAL SOCIETY — JUSTIFYING IT ALL WITH EVEN MORE ELABORATE IDEAS AND THEORIES OF WHITE RACIAL SUPERIORITY...

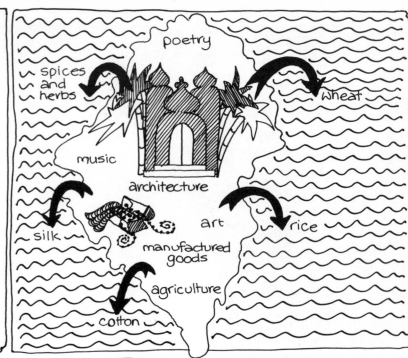

BRITAIN - LIKE OTHER COUNTRIES IN EUROPE - HAD ALWAYS WANTED TO GET HOLD OF INDIA'S BEAUTIFUL COTTONS AND SILKS, INDIGO, SPICES AND FINELY MADE GOODS.

THE BRITISH EAST INDIA COMPANY WAS SET UP IN THE 17th CENTURY TO DO THIS.

BY A MIXTURE OF TRICKERY AND WARFARE, IT TOOK CONTROL OVER THE TRADE WITH INDIA...

GRADUALLY BRITAIN GATHERED WEALTH TO FINANCE ITS OWN INDUSTRY, ESPECIALLY TEXTILES.

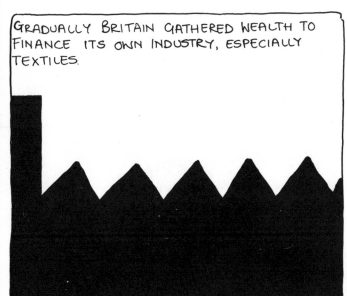

AS IT DID SO IT NO LONGER WANTED TO BUY INDIA'S FINE COTTONS. NOW IT WANTED TO KEEP THEM OUT AND FORCE INDIA TO BUY BRITISH MADE COTTONS — FOR BY THIS TIME THE BRITISH GOVERNMENT HAD TAKEN DIRECT CONTROL OVER INDIA FROM THE EAST INDIA COMPANY, (1857)

BRITAIN CHARGED HIGH IMPORT DUTIES ON FINISHED INDIAN COTTON GOODS ENTERING BRITAIN.

AS A RESULT MANY INDIAN WEAVERS LOST THEIR LIVING...

JUST AS EARLIER, THOSE WHO HAD REFUSED TO WORK FOR THE BRITISH EAST INDIA COMPANY HAD HAD THEIR LOOMS BURNT....

.... AND THEIR HANDS BROKEN

NOW THEY WERE DRIVEN OUT FROM ANY LIVELIHOOD ALTOGETHER

SOON COTTON WAS BEING WOVEN IN MANCHESTER FOR SALE TO INDIA ...

COTTON

FROM: MANCHESTER TO: INDIA

AND INDIA TURNED FROM BEING A PRODUCER OF BEAUTIFUL GOODS INTO A MARKET FOR INFERIOR COTTON GOODS...

... AND FROM A LAND THAT GREW FOOD TO FEED ALL THE PEOPLE OF INDIA ...

... INTO ONE THAT GREW <u>CASH CROPS</u> TO FEED THE FACTORIES OF BRITAIN ...

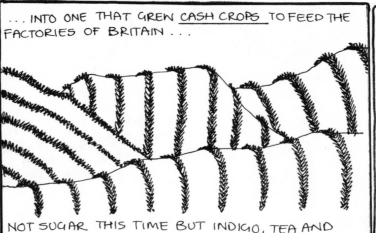

NOT SUGAR THIS TIME BUT INDIGO, TEA AND JUTE ....

.. EVER TRIED EATING TEA?

THE ENFORCED CASH CROP CYCLE TIED PEOPLE TO THE LAND, WITH JUST ENOUGH PAYMENT TO EXIST TO PLANT THE CROP AGAIN ...

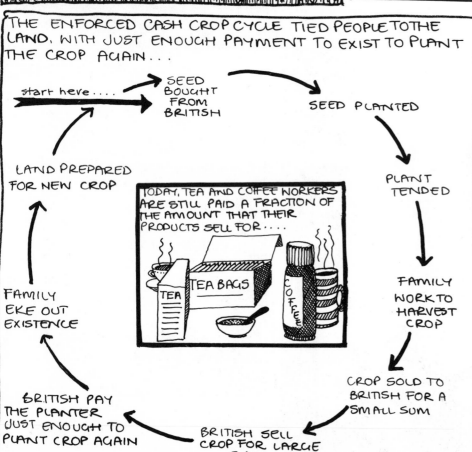

start here ....

SEED BOUGHT FROM BRITISH

SEED PLANTED

PLANT TENDED

FAMILY WORK TO HARVEST CROP

CROP SOLD TO BRITISH FOR A SMALL SUM

BRITISH SELL CROP FOR LARGE SUM

BRITISH PAY THE PLANTER JUST ENOUGH TO PLANT CROP AGAIN

FAMILY EKE OUT EXISTENCE

LAND PREPARED FOR NEW CROP

TODAY, TEA AND COFFEE WORKERS ARE STILL PAID A FRACTION OF THE AMOUNT THAT THEIR PRODUCTS SELL FOR ....

TEA   TEA BAGS   COFFEE

AS BRITAIN AND OTHER EUROPEAN COUNTRIES GREW RICHER AND MORE POWERFUL, THEY FORCED THIS SYSTEM OF PRODUCING THE <u>RAW MATERIALS</u> THEY WANTED FOR THEIR INDUSTRIES ONTO VAST REGIONS OF THE WORLD. ONE SUCH REGION WAS AFRICA, WHICH PRODUCES RAW MATERIALS SUCH AS

PALM OIL
SISAL
GROUND NUTS
COCOA BEANS
TIMBER
RUBBER . . . . .

GROUND NUTS

COCOA BEANS

PALM OIL

MOST IMPORTANT OF ALL TO EUROPE WERE AFRICA'S MINERALS;
GOLD
SILVER
DIAMONDS
COPPER
MANGANESE
WHICH WERE EXTRACTED IN VAST QUANTITIES BY EUROPE....

IT IS OFTEN WRITTEN THAT BRITISH COLONIALISM BROUGHT GREAT BENEFITS TO BLACK COUNTRIES....

BRINGING THE RAILWAYS TO HELP THE LOCALS THEY SAY...

THE REASON BEHIND THE BUILDING OF THE RAILWAYS WAS REALLY VERY DIFFERENT...

"Means of communication were not constructed in the Colonial Period so that Africans could visit their friends. More important still they were not laid down to facilitate internal trade in African commodities. All roads and railways led to the sea to make business possible for the timber companies, trading companies and agricultural firms for the white settlers."

Walter Rodney

"In most parts of Africa the Europeans who wanted to see a railroad built offered lashes as an ordinary wage, and more lashes for extra effort."
Walter Rodney.

AFRICA NOW BECAME THE HONEY POT TO WHICH ALL THE EUROPEAN POWERS WERE DRAWN...

AND BY THE END OF THE 19TH CENTURY, THE AFRICAN CONTINENT WAS CARVED UP BETWEEN THE EUROPEAN POWERS. BRITAIN TOOK THE LION'S SHARE. COLONIALISM HAD BECOME A WORLDWIDE SYSTEM.

13

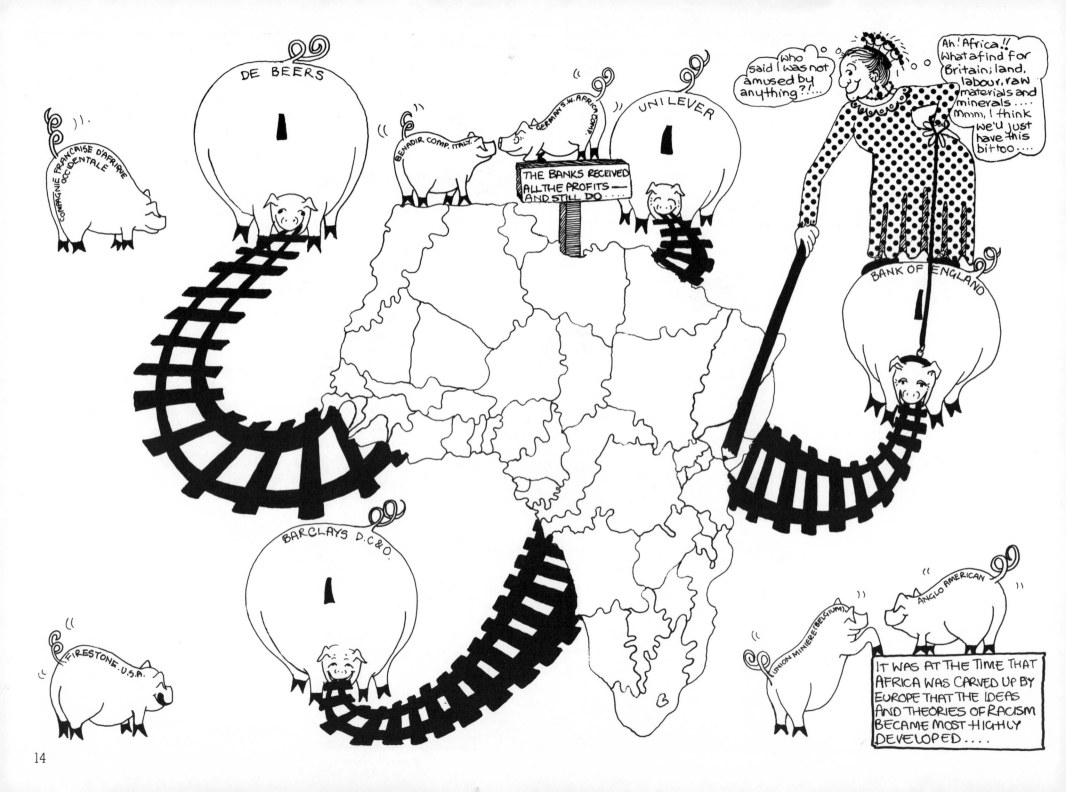

14

THE IDEAS BEHIND RACISM

IF YOU ARE WONDERING HOW A SMALL COUNTRY LIKE BRITAIN COULD HOLD TWO THIRDS OF THE WORLD IN THRALL...

ONE ANSWER WAS FORCE, BUT FORCE ALONE WAS NOT ENOUGH TO CONVINCE PEOPLE THAT THE BRITISH HAD A RIGHT TO RULE THEM....

IDEAS ARE ALSO WEAPONS, AND THE BRITISH USED THEM SHREWDLY....

TO MAKE SUBJECT PEOPLE A PARTY TO THEIR SUBJECTION BY GETTING THEM TO BELIEVE THAT THEIR CUSTOMS, RELIGIONS, CULTURE AND LANGUAGE WERE ALL INFERIOR TO THOSE OF THE COLONIALISTS...

16

* Thanks to Lewis Carroll.

WHOLE THEORIES WERE DEVELOPED IN WHICH DIFFERENT PEOPLES WERE 'GRADED' ACCORDING TO THEIR STATUS...

Years of research, which is far too obscure for you to follow, reveals these 'facts'....

1. White male Europeans are born to lead + rule.

2. Africans and Chinese can manage simple tasks.

3. Other people are doomed to extinction.

4. For proof of these theories I refer you to the learned work, "The Emperor's New Clothes"....

...nearer my God to thee...

...don't believe a word of this — go to Page 22 for my version!

THE ORDER OF THINGS

"IT IS PREDICTED THAT SOMEDAY THE MENIAL WORK OF THE UNIVERSE WILL ALL BE DONE BY CHINAMEN AND NEGROES WHILST THE WHITE RACE IS TO FILL THE HIGH PLACES OF THE EARTH, SQUEEZING OTHER RACES OUT OF EXISTENCE."
QUEENSLAND FIGARO. 6. OCT. 1883.

LOCAL PEOPLE WHO FOUGHT IN DEFENCE OF LAND AND LIVES WERE ALWAYS CALLED 'SAVAGE' OR 'TREACHEROUS' WHILE THE WHITE AGGRESSORS ARE ALWAYS REFERRED TO AS 'HEROES'....

THESE IDEAS WERE SHARPENED AND MADE INTO SCIENCES WITH FANCY NAMES....

EUGENICS: THIS WAS THE THEORY OF THE INNATE SUPERIORITY OF WHITE PEOPLE. ACCORDING TO IT ONLY CERTAIN PEOPLE OR GROUPS OF PEOPLE SHOULD BE ALLOWED TO HAVE CHILDREN.....

ANTHROPOMETRY: THIS WAS THE TERM FOR EUROPEANS MEASURING THE HEADS OF AFRICANS TO SEE HOW MUCH ROOM THEY HAD FOR BRAINS!

ALL THIS PROVED WAS HOW SMALL THE MINDS OF THE EUROPEANS WERE!....

PEAS

ANTHROPOLOGY:

Well... what's your verdict?...

It's...it's.... another culture! ....gasp.....

I didn't know there were any others.

most amusing....

what is it chaps?

fascinatin

I must be first to inform the ministry of culture about this.... we don't want the public to be 'confused' by it...

is it a bird ....is it a plane?

ALL THESE RACIST IDEAS PERCOLATED DOWN INTO THE SONGS, THE STORIES, THE PICTURES AND THE MUSIC HALLS, THE NEWSPAPER REPORTS, ADVERTISEMENTS, PARADES AND PROCESSIONS, IN FACT INTO EVERY WALK OF LIFE, UNTIL IT BECAME PART AND PARCEL OF BRITISH CULTURE....

EENY, MEENY MINY MO, CATCH A NIGGER BY THE TOE, IF HE SQUEALS LET HIM GO, EENY MEENY, MINY, MO

♪ ♪ ♪ ♪ "RULE BRITANNIA! BRITANNIA RULES THE WAVES"

Oh no! ... Not that song again ......

CARLYLE MACAULAY SHAKESPEARE

LAND of HOPE and GLORY ...

I can't take any more ....

DURHAM UNI. TO JOIN THE ZOO?

IN 1874 WHEN A COLLEGE IN SIERRA LEONE OBTAINED AN AFFILIATION TO DURHAM UNIVERSITY THE TIMES WROTE THAT DURHAM SHOULD NEXT AFFILIATE WITH LONDON ZOO...

GOSSAGES MAGICAL SOAP MAKES BLACK WHITE

TIMES QUEEN SNEEZES ~ SUN SETS MIGHT IS RIGHT!

EMPIRE DAY MUG

EMPIRE DAY PLATE

BUT EVEN AS THE EUROPEAN POWERS TOOK OVER VAST TERRITORIES OF AFRICA AND ASIA, THE PEOPLES OF THOSE COUNTRIES BEGAN TO RESIST MORE AND MORE STRONGLY, FOR THEIR LAND AND RESOURCES WERE BEING STOLEN FROM THEM.

THIS RESISTANCE TOOK MANY FORMS.......

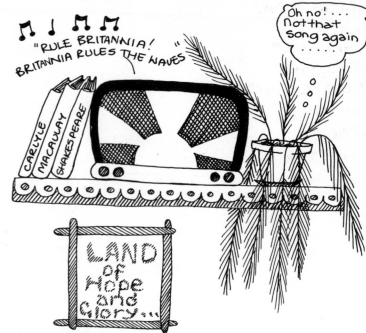

PEOPLE HAVE ALWAYS RESISTED AS WE HAVE SEEN. THE FORM OF RESISTANCE ALTERS AS THE NATURE OF COLONIALISM VARIES. LET'S LOOK AT THREE FORMS OF RESISTANCE...

AT THE LEVEL OF IDEOLOGY: PAN AFRICANISM... THIS WAS A MOVEMENT WHICH THREW OFF THE IDEAS OF WHITE SUPERIORITY THAT HAD BEEN DINNED INTO PEOPLE UNDER COLONIAL RULE. IT STRESSED INSTEAD SOLIDARITY BETWEEN AFRICAN, AFRO-CARIBBEAN AND AFRO-AMERICAN PEOPLES, ACROSS COLONIAL BOUNDARIES. IT CALLED FOR AFRICAN LIBERATION FROM WHITE RULE....

AT THE LEVEL OF MASS ACTION: SATYAGRAHA... THE BRITISH PRESENCE IN INDIA INCITED MASS CIVIL DISOBEDIENCE IN THE LATE 1920s. INDIAN DETERMINATION TO REGAIN CONTROL OF THEIR COUNTRY AND LIVES WAS GREATER THAN ALL THE BRITISH WEAPONS...

AT THE LEVEL OF ARMED STRUGGLE: ONE OF THE FIRST GUERILLA WARS FOUGHT SUCCESSFULLY FOR INDEPENDENCE AND FREEDOM WAS THAT OF THE LAND AND FREEDOM ARMY — THE MAU MAU IN KENYA...

I know they are here somewhere....

THE STRENGTH OF RESISTANCE AROUND THE WORLD WAS SUCH THAT IT BECAME TOO COSTLY FOR BRITAIN TO PUT DOWN AND BY THE END OF THE 1939/45 WAR BRITAIN WAS UNABLE TO HOLD ONTO ITS COLONIES MUCH LONGER, AND WAS RELUCTANTLY "GRANTING" INDEPENDENCE.... NOT HOWEVER BEFORE THE DAMAGE HAD BEEN DONE....

INDEPENDENCE! WHAT IT MEANS FOR US IS: A PEOPLE WITHOUT LAND, A LAND WITHOUT FOOD, A WORKFORCE WITHOUT THE CAPITAL TO ACTIVATE IT.....

AT A MIDLANDS FOUNDRY THINGS LOOKED VERY BLEAK:

CALENDAR.
1947

FEB:

1	2	3	4	5	6	7	8
9	10	11	12	13	14	15	16
17	18	19	20	21	22	23	24
25	26		28				

..."I WOULD EVEN TAKE ON AN ARMLESS, LEGLESS, COLOURED MAN!..."

...and if he has any brothers or cousins I'd take them on too!

HAVING HELPED TO WIN BRITAIN'S WAR.....

NOW THEY WERE ASKED TO WIN THE PEACE FOR BRITAIN TOO.....

IN THE WEST INDIES, WHILE LONDON TRANSPORT WAS RECRUITING WORKERS FOR THE BUSES AND TUBES, HEALTH MINISTER ENOCH POWELL(!) WAS LOOKING FOR NURSES TO WORK FOR THE N.H.S....

COME TO BRITAIN FOR JOBS...

THE JOBS THE BRITISH WON'T DO...

what does it say on the back of the placard, I can't see it clearly?...

I can't see from here, let's fill in these application forms—come on!

FROM AROUND 1950, BLACK PEOPLE BEGAN TO BE USED AS PAWNS IN A NEW GAME DEVISED BY THE BRITISH..... IT WAS CALLED

"YOU CAN'T WIN!"— ANY NUMBER OF PEOPLE COULD PLAY — AS LONG AS THEY WERE BLACK...

RULES OF "YOU CAN'T WIN"...
1. YOU MUST BE BLACK
2. YOU MUST STICK TO THE RULES SET BY BRITAIN
3. YOU CANNOT QUESTION YOUR POSITION
4. YOU MUST TAKE ANY WORK OFFERED
5. YOU MUST LIVE ON THE MARGINS OF SOCIETY
6. THE DICE MUST BE MADE IN BRITAIN....

RACISM BECOMES RESPECTABLE

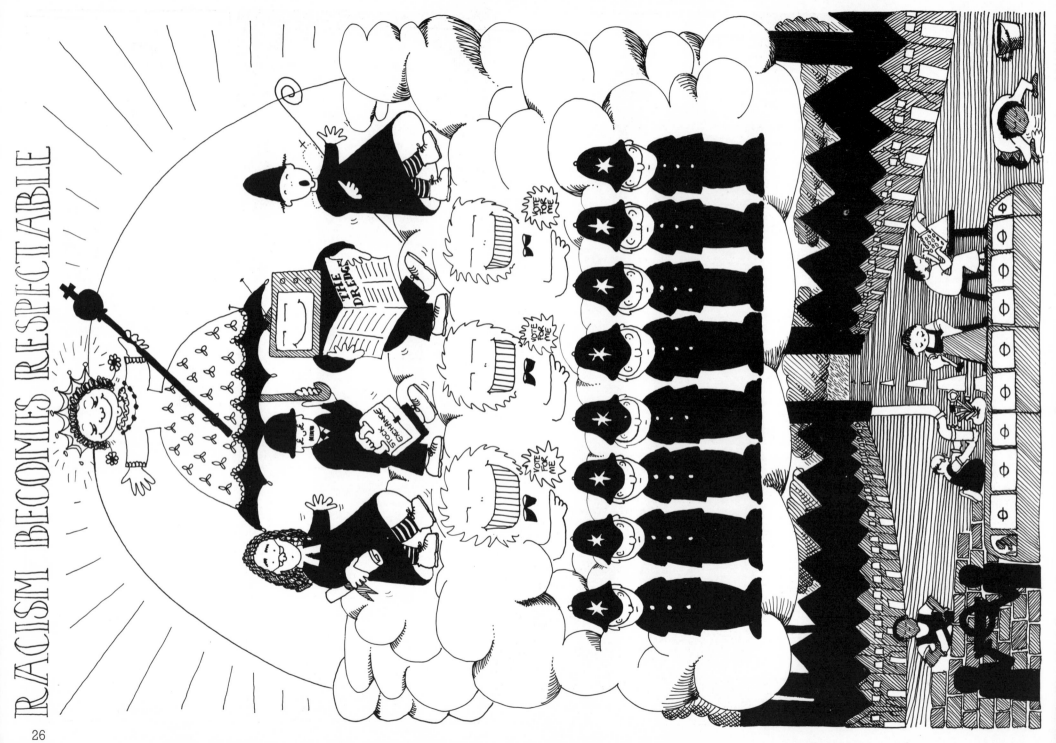

At first, when Britain wanted all the workers it could get, it passed the 1948 Nationality Act. This gave all commonwealth citizens equality and rights to come and go....

The labour of black workers was used to build the new Britain cheaply and keep its services running. They worked in places such as hospitals and foundries and on public transport...

Yes, we'll take you on as a qualified doctor and save the £15,000 your training cost...

We'll take you on in the textile trade... we can pay you less than white workers...

And we'll take you on to clean the underground tunnels at night, for some reason we don't get many applications...

Despite the efforts of black workers, they received no recognition when it came to their own needs...

THE ONLY HOUSING THEY COULD GET WAS OLD, DILAPIDATED HOUSES IN RUN DOWN INNER-CITY AREAS.

THE MYTH GREW THAT THE PRESENCE OF THE BLACK POPULATION WAS THE CAUSE OF THE HOUSING SHORTAGE ....

THE REALITY WAS THAT THE BLACK COMMUNITY WAS FORCED TO TAKE THE HOUSING THAT NO ONE ELSE WANTED TO LIVE IN ....

THE ONLY SCHOOLING THEY COULD GET WAS IN RUN-DOWN, OVERCROWDED SCHOOLS...

IN THE MEANTIME, AS THE BOOM OF THE '50s ENDED, THE LABOUR POWER OF BLACK WORKERS WAS NO LONGER NEEDED AND SO LAWS TO CUT DOWN IMMIGRATION WERE PASSED......

Jane's raffia work has got very low marks since those black kids came...

THE MYTH GREW THAT THE PRESENCE OF BLACK CHILDREN WAS THE PROBLEM....

THE REALITY WAS THAT THE AUTHORITIES' RESPONSE WAS TO PANDER TO THE WISHES OF RACIALISTS RATHER THAN TO OFFER SUFFICIENT SERVICES TO ALL ....

...BY SUCCESSIVE LABOUR AND CONSERVATIVE GOVERNMENTS...

AND WITH EACH PARTY VYING WITH THE OTHER AS TO WHO COULD HAVE THE FEWEST BLACK PEOPLE IN BRITAIN.

VOTE FOR ME; I'LL VOTE TO KEEP DEPENDENT BLACK RELATIVES OUT OF BRITAIN!

VOTE FOR ME; I'LL MAKE SURE WOMEN CAN'T BRING THEIR FIANCÉS HERE!

VOTE FOR ME; I'LL KEEP OLD AND YOUNG BLACK PEOPLE OUT... THEY USE THE FACILITIES MOST!....

VOTE FOR ME; I'LL MAKE IT HARDER FOR WOMEN TO COME TO BRITAIN.... THEY MIGHT HAVE CHILDREN HERE!......

I'm not, um, certain of course but these policies may lead to some tension...

GOVERNMENT POLICIES WERE SEEN TO BE GIVING TACIT RESPECTABILITY TO RACISM AND THE WHITE RACISTS ROSE TO THE OCCASION .... 1958....

BUT NONE OF THE REAL REASONS FOR IMMIGRATION CONTROL WERE TOLD TO THE PUBLIC. INSTEAD THEY WERE OFFERED A VERY DIFFERENT STORY...

INSTEAD OF COUNTERING THE RACIALIST IDEAS GROWING UP, AND ADMITTING THEIR OWN RESPONSIBILITY; THE POLITICIANS JOINED IN, AND THE 'POLITER' ONES MADE IT ALL INTO A PHILOSOPHY...

"WE MUST DIGEST THEM A MOUTHFUL AT A TIME..."

"WITHOUT INTEGRATION LIMITATION IS INEXCUSABLE; WITHOUT LIMITATION INTEGRATION IS IMPOSSIBLE."

ROY HATTERSLEY 1965

AND SO THE 'COMMONSENSE' ANSWER GREW THAT IF YOU HAD FEWER NUMBERS YOU HAD LESS OF A PROBLEM ..... JUST THE SAME SORT OF ANSWER THAT HITLER HAD FOR THE JEWS...

OTHERS WERE LESS POLITE AND, PRETENDING TO SPEAK FOR THE COMMON PEOPLE, STOKED THEIR RACIST FEARS AND FANTASIES.

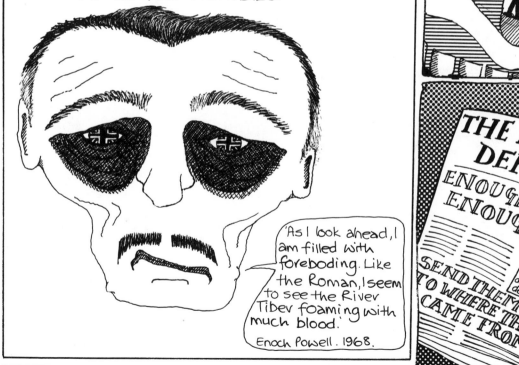

'As I look ahead, I am filled with foreboding. Like the Roman, I seem to see the River Tiber foaming with much blood.'

Enoch Powell. 1968.

THE DAILY DEPTHS

ENOUGH IS ENOUGH!

SEND THEM BACK TO WHERE THEY CAME FROM!

We sink to depths that defy belief...

Patrials....
Preconditions
...reluctance
...swamp
tide...

Moderation...
Integrate?...
Caution...
Rejection?...

JARGON ABOUNDED IN THE REVERED INSTITUTIONS OF GOVERNMENT, BUT THE PRESS WERE QUICK TO GET THE POINT....

PRESS, T.V AND RADIO TOOK THEIR CUE FROM THE POLITICIANS, PURVEYING AND POPULARISING RACIST IDEAS AMONG THE PUBLIC....

Minister says — "Keep the Blacks out!" ... read all about it!!...

M.P SPEAKS OUT TODAY

If it's in the paper and quoted from politicians it must be true!!...

THE DREDGE

STOP THE FLOOD OR WE'LL BE SWAMPED BY THE TIDE

WHATEVER THEIR PARTY COLOURS, AND WHATEVER PAPER THEY WRAP THEIR STATEMENTS IN — NOTHING CAN REMOVE THOSE TELL TALE STAINS OF RACISM FROM THEIR WHITER THAN WHITE MANIFESTOS.

BLACK PEOPLE DIDN'T TAKE ALL THIS LYING DOWN, AND IN AN ATTEMPT TO APPEASE THEM AND THE FEW WHITE CRITICS THERE WERE, THE GOVERNMENT INTRODUCED LEGISLATION AIMED AT INTEGRATION, EVEN WHILE PASSING LEGISLATION TO CONTROL IMMIGRATION OF BLACK PEOPLE INTO THE COUNTRY......

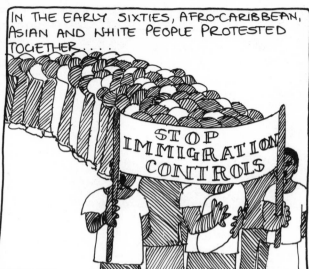

IN THE EARLY SIXTIES, AFRO-CARIBBEAN, ASIAN AND WHITE PEOPLE PROTESTED TOGETHER.....

STOP IMMIGRATION CONTROLS

This is just for you!...

This is just for you!...

RACE RELATIONS ACT

IMMIGRATION CONTROL

With love from the Labour Party

RACE RELATIONS ACT: 1965...

RACE RELATIONS ACT: 1968...

RACE RELATIONS ACT: 1976...

If you're wondering what the Acts did....

It took 3 years to allow an investigation into the Immigration Service...

Under the clause that investigation can be initiated, little has happened...

...often based on conciliation or little fines...

The Race Relations Acts are weak and toothless...

It takes too long to get a decision...

A house or a job would be gone!...

The punishments are too slight...

The 'proper channels' don't work.....we must take up issues for ourselves.....

RACIST BRITAIN

EMPLOYMENT

THERE WAS ENOUGH WORK FOR ALL IN THE EARLY 1950's ... BLACK PEOPLE GOT WORK — BUT ON VERY DIFFERENT TERMS TO WHITE WORKERS ...

CONTINUING DISCRIMINATION MEANT THAT THE BLACK COMMUNITY TOOK THE INITIATIVE FOR CHANGE THEMSELVES. OFTEN THEY UNIONISED A FACTORY AND CALLED FOR STRIKE ACTION OVER CONDITIONS OF WORK AND RACISM ....

WHITE WORKERS AND UNIONS RARELY GAVE SUPPORT TO BLACK WORKERS. THEY RELIED ON THEIR OWN COMMUNITIES. THEIR ACTIONS MADE A LOT OF SENSE TO THOSE WHO SHARED THEIR HISTORY ....

THEY WERE PAID LESS FOR THE SAME WORK:

TEMPLES GAVE FOOD AND SUPPORT THROUGHOUT THE STRIKE:

SHOPKEEPERS GAVE CREDIT:

Here, take a pair each for your children in this snowy weather!

LANDLORDS WAIVED THE RENT:

THEY WERE ASKED TO WORK LONGER HOURS:

WEST INDIAN AND ASIAN COMMUNITY SUPPORT FOR EACH OTHER WAS ALSO EVIDENT IN THE STRIKES. THE BENEFIT OF SHARED EXPERIENCE HELPED WORKERS IN THE FOLLOWING STRIKES;

1965 COURTAULDS (PRESTON)
1965 WOOLFS (SOUTHALL)
1969 NEWBY FOUNDRY (WEST BROMWICH)
1972 MANSFIELD HOSIERY MILLS (LOUGHBORO')
1973 HARWOOD CASH LAWN MILLS (MANSFIELD)
1973 STANDARD TELEPHONES AND CABLES (NEW SOUTHGATE)
1973 PERIVALE GUTERMAN (SOUTHALL)

WOMEN FOUGHT SIDE BY SIDE WITH THE MEN AND IN SOLIDARITY WITH THEM — AT HOME, ON THE PICKET LINE AND IN THE FACTORIES, AND WOMEN WERE IN THE FOREFRONT IN A NUMBER OF STRIKES SUCH AS:

1974 IMPERIAL TYPEWRITERS (LEICESTER)
1976 GRUNWICK (NORTH LONDON)
1979 FUTTERS (NORTH LONDON)
1979-80 CHIX (SLOUGH)

THEY WERE DENIED PROMOTION AND ASKED TO WORK BELOW THEIR QUALIFICATIONS ....

Well, this puts my Philosophy Degree to the test ....

TODAY IT IS NOT SO MUCH THESE ISSUES THAT ARE AT THE FOREFRONT, BUT UNEMPLOYMENT ....

FIGURES FOR UNEMPLOYED MALES (1981).

WHITE	9.7%
WEST INDIAN	20.6%
ASIAN	16.9%
OTHERS	13.9%

HOUSING

BLACK PEOPLE WERE BROUGHT INTO BRITAIN AS WORKERS — BUT NO PROVISION WAS MADE FOR WHERE THEY SHOULD LIVE. LANDLORDS REFUSED TO RENT THEM ROOMS. BUILDING SOCIETIES WOULD NOT LEND MONEY. THEY COULD NOT GET COUNCIL HOUSING. SO THEY HAD TO POOL THEIR RESOURCES, BUY BETWEEN THEM AND SHARE DILAPIDATED HOUSES THAT NO ONE ELSE WOULD WANT — WHICH OF COURSE WAS EXCUSE ENOUGH FOR LOCAL AUTHORITIES TO DRIVE THEM OUT AGAIN — FOR OVERCROWDING!

RACISTS OFTEN BLOCKED ACCESS TO PRIVATE HOUSING

FOR SALE TO WHITES ONLY

AND AS FOR COUNCILS...

RESIDENTIAL QUALIFICATIONS WERE USED TO KEEP BLACK TENANTS OUT. IT COULD TAKE ANYTHING FROM 1–10 YEARS JUST TO GET ON THE WAITING LIST

CALENDAR 1951

Come back in 1956....

COUNCILS WERE FOUND TO BE MARKING THEIR RECORDS SO THAT BLACK FAMILIES GOT OFFERED THE WORST HOUSING..

Ah hello Mr Lloyd, funny you should phone today...

I've found a house for you... It needs a little attention perhaps, but is a big improvement on where you are now...

The worst thing most white people get through their mailbox is a bill or two.... For black residents on some estates, deliveries of urine and faeces and petrol-soaked rags come as regularly....

WELCOME

IN DECEMBER 1984, HOMELESS FAMILIES — MANY OF THEM BLACK — OCCUPIED CAMDEN TOWN HALL FOR A MONTH AFTER A BENGALI MOTHER AND HER TWO CHILDREN DIED IN A FIRE IN A RUN-DOWN BED AND BREAKFAST HOTEL WHERE THE COUNCIL HAD TEMPORARILY PLACED THEM. MANY HOMELESS FAMILIES HAVE TO LIVE LIKE THIS IN A NUMBER OF TOWNS AND BOROUGHS FOR LONG PERIODS OF TIME.

260 INCIDENTS OF RACIAL HARASSMENT WERE REPORTED TO THE TOWER HAMLETS HOUSING DEPARTMENT IN THE NINE MONTHS UP TO DECEMBER 1984. THAT'S ALMOST ONE EACH DAY.... AND THOSE ARE ONLY THE REPORTED INCIDENTS...

IN JANUARY 1984 THE C.R.E. PUBLISHED A REPORT CONTAINING EVIDENCE THAT HACKNEY HOUSING DEPARTMENT (LONDON) HAD BEEN RACIST IN ITS ALLOCATION OF COUNCIL HOUSING.

How many evictions have there been of white tenants due to their racist behaviour toward black tenants?

By February 1985 there had been just one eviction from a council-run estate.

1

0

EDUCATION

INSTEAD OF PROVISION BEING MADE AVAILABLE FOR ASIAN CHILDREN IN THEIR LOCAL AREA, THEY WERE 'BUSSED' TO OTHER AREAS FOR SCHOOLING. THIS MEANT A LONG AND TIRING DAY AND BEING VULNERABLE TO ATTACK...

I wish I went to school with my friends around here...

I wish I lived nearer to my friends at school...

I wish I didn't have to wait for the bus home...

FROM 1963 ASIAN CHILDREN WERE BEING 'BUSSED' AS A POLICY... AFRO-CARIBBEAN CHILDREN WERE ALSO GIVEN A CLEAR MESSAGE THAT THEY WERE NOT WANTED EITHER... THEY WERE LABELLED 'EDUCATIONALLY SUBNORMAL', WERE SENT TO THE LOWER CLASSES IN THE SCHOOL AND OFTEN TO SCHOOLS FOR 'MALADJUSTED' CHILDREN...

I am the Educational Psychologist. I say that this child is definitely maladjusted and should be moved to the new purpose built unit on the other side of town!

I am the child, and I say that anyone who can live happily in a society that forces me and my family to have bad housing, no work, or only dirty, low paid work, nowhere to play, run-down schools and no jobs at the end of it, must be maladjusted and probably lives in a big house on the other side of town from me!...

The 'A' Team

BOTH THESE ISSUES LED TO STRUGGLES IN THE BLACK COMMUNITIES, AGAINST THE RACISM IN EDUCATION, AND FOR BETTER PROVISION FOR ALL. THEY SET UP SCHOOLS FOR THE CHILDREN TO TAKE PART IN AT HOLIDAY TIMES, EVENINGS AND AT WEEKENDS...

Marcus Garvey
Malcolm X
Martin Luther King
Mahatma Gandhi

This is a very different version of history to the one I've been taught...

TODAY THE RACISM IN SCHOOLING CONTINUES. NEW PHRASES AND WORDS FOR THE SAME IDEAS...

1960's = "unrealistic aspirations"

1970's = "underachievement and behaviour problems"

1980's = "cognitive deficiencies"

POLICE

EVER SINCE THEY CAME TO BRITAIN, BLACK PEOPLE HAVE HAD TO CONTEND WITH THE RACISM OF THE POLICE AND THE MISUSE OF POLICE POWERS AGAINST THEM. THE FIRST BOOKLET ON THE SUBJECT BY A BLACK AUTHOR WAS PUBLISHED OVER 20 YEARS AGO....

FROM HUNDREDS OF EXAMPLES HERE ARE A COUPLE OF TRUE STORIES...

ONCE UPON A TIME... 1978, IN HACKNEY (LONDON) A YOUNG BOY WAS ON HIS WAY TO SCHOOL,

Where are you going eh?

to school!

Oh yeah! So where's your passport eh?

HE WAS TAKEN TO THE POLICE STATION AND ILLEGALLY HELD FOR ONE AND A HALF HOURS.

IN JUNE 1983 AT A CHINGFORD SCHOOL, POLICE ASKED FOR, AND WERE GIVEN, THE NAMES AND ADDRESSES OF ALL THE BLACK CHILDREN, FOLLOWING AN ATTACK ON AN ELDERLY WHITE LADY IN THE AREA...

Oh yes, we've established a clear line of enquiry— we want details of all your black pupils!...

ANYONE CAN BE ARRESTED 'ON SUSPICION' BY THE POLICE...

36.47.1. 106.8.

Yeah, the service has been cut back!

You've been here a long time...

POLICE FIND TWO HEADS ARE BETTER THAN ONE WHEN SUBMITTING EVIDENCE....

It was like this Your honour...

Yes! It was like that — he's right...

Oh yeah! And then that happened..

Yes, I can confirm that...

AND THE POLICE ARE BACKED UP BY THE COURTS...

As THIS MAGISTRATE FELT FREE TO COMMENT...

Black youths who come to the West End to shop, ask for trouble!...

WHAT ALL THIS MEANS IS THAT BLACK YOUTH HAVE TO PROVE THEY'RE INNOCENT OF WHATEVER THE POLICE ACCUSE THEM OF. IT'S NOT THE POLICE WHO HAVE TO PROVE THEM GUILTY...

IF AFRO-CARIBBEAN YOUTH ARE SUSPECTED OF THEFT AND MUGGING JUST BY BEING ON THE STREET...

ASIANS ARE EQUALLY SUSPECTED OF BEING ILLEGAL IMMIGRANTS, AND POLICE CARRY OUT RAIDS AND PASSPORT CHECKS AT WILL...

ON 30 JUNE 1980 IN NELSON LANCASHIRE, TWO ASIAN GIRLS AGED 9 AND 12 YEARS OLD WERE DRAGGED OUT OF SCHOOL AS ILLEGAL IMMIGRANTS.

SCHOOL EXIT

WHILE POLICE SWAMP BLACK EVENTS BY FORCE OF NUMBERS (OVER 1,600 POLICE WERE AT THE NOTTING HILL CARNIVAL IN 1976)....

THEY ARE NOWHERE TO BE SEEN WHEN IT COMES TO RACIST ATTACKS....

Now then, what's all the fuss and panic about claims of an alleged racist attack eh? Move along there in an orderly fashion or I'll have you for obstruction!....

IMMIGRATION CONTROLS

Let me tell you about my uncle, aunt and my cousin....

My Uncle came to work in Britain in the 1950's. Once he had saved to support them, my aunt and cousin applied to join him...

MY AUNT AND COUSIN WAITED 19 MONTHS FOR AN INTERVIEW...

THE ENTRY CLEARANCE OFFICERS ARE OBSESSED WITH DETAILS THAT DON'T FIT TOGETHER, EAGER TO FIND A REASON TO REFUSE ENTRY...

Ah ha! Got you... You say you have a black + white bullock and a brown cow...

...but your son says you have a white and black bullock and a brown cow... you are obviously not really mother and son at all!....

E.C.O.

HAQ CASE IX
HAQ CASE VIII
HAQ CASE VII
HAQ CASE VI
HAQ CASE V
HAQ CASE IV
HAQ CASE III
HAQ CASE II
HAQ CASE I

HAQ CASE VOL. I
HAQ CASE VOL. II
HAQ CASE VOL III

BUT FOR THOSE WHO DO COME TO ENGLAND — WHAT HAPPENS TO THEM?

PASSPORTS

Thank you...

Just wait over there...

IMAGINE IT; MY AUNT HAD TO GO 200 MILES TO THE BIG CITY TO BE INTERVIEWED VIA AN INTERPRETER WHO SPOKE IN A DIFFERENT DIALECT....

INTERVIEWS ARE NOT TAPED: FILES BUILD UP AND SO DO THE MISTAKES THAT THE E.C.Os MAKE AT EACH INTERVIEW — THEY DO NOT GET ERASED OF COURSE....

WELCOME TO HEATHROW

Oh yeah? ...well, we'll wait and see....

Did you know that Immigration Officers expect to receive answers to questions they haven't asked?...

...AND UNTIL 1979 WOMEN WERE FORCED TO HAVE INTERNAL EXAMINATIONS TO VERIFY 'VIRGINITY'...

But for people who are here... all's well that ends well, eh?

NO!

As we saw on the previous page the threat to their security continues here from the Police...

Their troubles were just beginning....

PASS LAW SOCIETY:

I was born here but my mum has to produce documents all the time

What for?

Oh, you know! Those little details of life...

Like Housing...

Let me see your papers and identification first!...

I would like to apply for housing for my family....

Health Care...

Never mind that.... papers and identification first!...

My wife is sick and needs nursing care in hospital...

Education....

Let me see your papers first!...

I wish to enrol my son at the local school...

The Message is very clear...

Prove It!!

I have a right to live here...

Is BRITAIN CREATING A PASS LAW SOCIETY AKIN TO SOUTH AFRICA'S APARTHEID SOCIETY...?

MEDIA

IN THE MEDIA NEWS ABOUT BLACK PEOPLE IS OFTEN PRESENTED AS BAD NEWS....

PEOPLE LIKE ENOCH POWELL ARE GIVEN A LOT OF EXPOSURE IN THE MEDIA – BLACK PEOPLE AND ANTI-RACISTS DO NOT GET THE SAME TIME....

BLACK PEOPLE ARE USED AS THE BUTT OF JOKES IN 'SHOWS' AND CARTOONS AND ABUSED IN SHOWS SUCH AS THE 'BLACK AND WHITE MINSTRELS'...

IT WAS ENOUGH TO MAKE YOU SEE SPOTS BEFORE YOUR EYES...

RACIST IMAGES ARE USED IN THE ADVERTISING OF PRODUCTS...

WATCH OUT ON YOUR LIBRARY SHELVES FOR BOOKS THAT SHOULD BE THROWN AWAY...

OR, PERHAPS YOU COULD GET TOGETHER WITH SOME FRIENDS AND WRITE YOUR OWN STORIES WHICH LOOK AT LIFE IN A VERY DIFFERENT WAY?...

TELEVISION LIKES TO SEE ITSELF AS THE WINDOW ON THE WORLD. HOWEVER IT HAS ONLY TWO APPROACHES TO BLACK PEOPLE AND IT DOESN'T ANALYSE EITHER...

1 ... TO PATRONIZE THEM:

2 ... TO PUT THEM DOWN:

IN NEITHER CASE ARE BLACK PEOPLE EVER ASKED FOR THEIR POINT OF VIEW....

IN 1981 THE HOME OFFICE REPORTED...

"WEST INDIANS ARE 36 TIMES MORE LIKELY, AND ASIANS ARE 50 TIMES MORE LIKELY TO BE ATTACKED AS A RESULT OF RACIAL VIOLENCE IN BRITAIN...."

MR AND MRS SHAH, LIVING IN THE MIDLANDS, HAD BOARDED UP THEIR HOUSE FOR 9 YEARS AGAINST ATTACKS. IN DESPERATION THEY TOOK REFUGE BY DRIVING AWAY AND LIVING IN THEIR CAR ON A LAY-BY TO AVOID RACIST ATTACKS...

DESPITE BEING ABLE TO IDENTIFY THEIR ATTACKERS TO THE POLICE... THE POLICE INSTEAD CHARGED MR SHAH WITH CRIMINAL DAMAGE AND CAUSING A BREACH OF THE PEACE!

Well, well, if it isn't Mr Shah..... We want a word with you...

A YOUNG BLACK COUPLE WERE OUT WITH THEIR BABY WHEN SHE WAS SHOT IN THE EYE FROM A PASSING CAR. THEY RUSHED THEIR BABY TO NEWHAM GENERAL HOSPITAL WHERE SHE HAD A THREE HOUR OPERATION TO REMOVE THE PELLET FROM HER SKULL...

We have no reason to suspect that the motive was racial....

Who's got their eyes bandaged .... him or me?!

ON NOV. 20TH 1981 MOHAMMED 'A', A TAXI DRIVER IN BRADFORD WAS MURDERED IN HIS TAXI.....

EXTREME RIGHT WING POLITICAL GROUPS ARE ORGANIZING AND ENCOURAGING RACIAL VIOLENCE. GROUPS SUCH AS THE NATIONAL FRONT AND THE BRITISH MOVEMENT ARE AT THE FOREFRONT.

THE N.F. AND B.M. BELIEVE THAT BRITAIN SHOULD ONLY BE LIVED IN BY WHITE BRITISH PEOPLE.... PREFERABLY ONLY THOSE WHO THINK AND LOOK LIKE THEM. IMAGINE IT....

N.F.

THIS IS WHAT THE NAZI PARTY BELIEVED WAS GOOD FOR GERMANY IN THE 1930's. IF YOUR EYES, FACE, HAIR, SKIN, THOUGHTS AND BELIEFS DIDN'T FIT INTO HITLER'S PLAN YOU WERE DEPORTED, GASSED OR TORTURED....

watch the one second from the left...

TODAY IN BRITAIN THE NATIONAL FRONT AIMS TO INTIMIDATE, TERRORIZE AND VIOLATE THE BLACK COMMUNITY TILL THEY CAN STAND THE PRESSURE NO LONGER AND LEAVE....

OF COURSE THEY COULD NOT DO THIS IF THE POLICE DID NOT TURN A BLIND EYE ...

VIOLENT RACIALISM IS BEING SOLD TO YOUNG PEOPLE...

FOOTBALL GRO

Did your team lose lads? Aaah, never mind.... kick a black head in instead of a football. We always score!

RACISTS SUPPORT BANDS WHICH EXPRESS THEIR PERSPECTIVE IN SONG....

"THERE AIN'T NO BLACK IN THE UNION JACK"....

THE ANTI NAZI LEAGUE WAS FORMED IN 1977 BY PEOPLE WHO OPPOSED NAZI IDEAS AND RACISM. MANY SUB GROUPS WERE FORMED SUCH AS SCHOOLKIDS AGAINST THE NAZIS — WOMEN AGAINST THE NAZIS ... DO YOU REMEMBER?

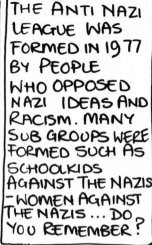

NF = NO FUN

BLACK COMMUNITIES HAVE ORGANIZED THEMSELVES TO RESIST RACIST ATTACKS IN THE LIGHT OF POLICE INDIFERENCE...

HOWEVER, THE POLICE ARE EAGER TO ARREST BLACK YOUTH FOR DEFENDING THEIR COMMUNITIES...

THE RESULTING TRIALS WERE LONG AND PROTRACTED. BUT IN SPITE OF BIAS FROM THE JUDICIARY....

THE JURY HAS OFTEN FOUND IN FAVOUR OF PEOPLE DEFENDING THEIR OWN COMMUNITIES...

41

Glossary

Activate: To get something moving or working.

Agricultural society: A society whose economy is based on, and most of whose people are engaged in, cultivating the land, growing crops and raising live stock for their own consumption.

Anthropology: The study of different forms of human society and culture.

Apartheid: Officially defined as separate development for whites and blacks respectively, but in fact the system by which a small minority of whites has political, social and economic domination over a vast majority of non-white people in South Africa.

Capital: Capitalism is an economic system based on the private ownership of what are called the means of production (that is all the basic requirements for producing goods — raw materials, machinery and labour.) The main aim of capitalists is to produce goods so as to sell them at a profit. Capital itself consists of accumulated wealth, generated by using money to bring labour and raw materials together, in order to make products for sale.

Cash crops: Produce grown for sale for money on the world market, and not for home consumption.

Colonialism: The process by which people from the major trading nations took over and settled in other countries to ensure that the 'mother country' was supplied with raw materials for its industries. The colonies also provided a market for the finished goods produced in the 'mother country'. Britain's empire consisted of the colonies over which it ruled.

Commodities: These can be any goods produced in order to be bought and sold, but generally associated with agricultural products and raw materials.

Conciliation: To reconcile, bring together mutually opposed views; to make friends between people. For those who suffered the immediate and concrete effects of racial discrimination, this was an intolerably slow and ineffective method of getting any justice.

Discrimination: In this context, to treat one group of people (marked out by their origin or skin colour) less favourably than others — perhaps through laws or social policies which only apply to them.

Exploit: exploitation: In this book the term has two broad meanings:
(a) the exploitation of men and women which occurs when more wealth is obtained from using their labour power to produce goods, than is handed back to them in the form of wages, for example. This is how profit is made.
(b) the exploitation of a region's raw materials and natural resources — in other words, taking measures on a large scale to increase the amount and availability of raw materials for use in the production of goods.

Guerillas: A popular army or army of the people, fighting to overcome unjust rule, often that of an occupying power.

Ideology: A general system of ideas, beliefs and theories — a way of thinking — based on a particular interpretation of society and history.

Import duty: A tax on goods brought into a country.

Integration: In this context, to fit black people into white society.

Plantation: A large agricultural estate or farm, organised on industrial lines, where one particular crop is intensively cultivated by enslaved or semi-slave workers.

Profit: The reward and goal of the capitalist, the owner of the means of production; the wealth left to the capitalist after all the costs of production have been paid for. *See also* **exploitation**.

Raw materials: Substances in their unprocessed state which are a major ingredient for the production of goods. Examples of raw materials include rubber, iron ore, cotton, coal, etc.

Further reading

An asterisk (*) indicates more difficult texts

General
L. Huberman, *Man's worldly goods: the story of the wealth of nations*, Part 1 (New York, Monthly Review Press, 1968)
Institute of Race Relations, *Roots of racism* (London, IRR, 1982)
Institute of Race Relations, *Patterns of racism* (London, IRR, 1982)
* A. Sivanandan, *A different hunger: writings on black resistance* (London, Pluto, 1982)

Chapter 1
* E. Galeano, *The open veins of Latin America* (New York, Monthly Review Press, 1973)
L. Honychurch, *The Caribbean people*, Book 1 (London, Nelson Caribbean, 1979)

Chapter 2
E. Brathwaite and A. Phillips, *The people who came*, Book 3 (Harlow, Longman Caribbean, 1972)
* Philip Foner, *History of Black Americans* (London and New York, Greenwood, 1975)
Alex Haley, *Roots* (London, Hutchinson, 1977), fiction
* Richard Hart, *Blacks in bondage: slaves who abolished slavery* (Jamaica, Institute of Social and Economic Research, 1980)
D. Killingray, *The slave trade* (London, Harrap, 1974)
J. Lester, *To be a slave* (Harlow, Longman, 1970), short stories
Milton McFarlane, *Cudjoe the Maroon* (London, Allison & Busby, 1977)
* Eric Williams, *Capitalism and slavery* (London, Longman, 1974)

Chapter 3
Mulk Raj Anand, *Two leaves and a bud* (Bombay, Kutub, 1966)
Basil Davidson, *Discovering Africa's past* (Harlow, Longman, 1978)
Susan George and Nigel Paige, *Food for Beginners* (London, Writers & Readers, 1982)
* E. Hobsbawm, *The age of revolution: Europe 1789-1848* (London, Weidenfeld & Nicolson, 1962)

* E. Hobsbawm, *The age of capital 1848-1875* (London, Weidenfeld & Nicolson, 1975)
Musimgrafik, *Where monsoons meet: cartoon history of Malaya* (London, Grassroots, 1979)
* Walter Rodney, *How Europe underdeveloped Africa* (London, Bogle L'Ouverture, 1972)

Chapter 4
Anti-Apartheid News, *Drawing the line; cartoons against apartheid* (London, AAM, 1984)
* Frantz Fanon, *Black skins, white masks* (London, Macgibbon & Kee, 1968)
D. Hiro, *Black British: White British* (London, Eyre & Spottiswoode, 1971), Chapter 11
* V.G. Kiernan, *The Lords of Human Kind: European attitudes to the outside world in the imperial age* (London, Weidenfeld & Nicolson, 1969)
Chris Searle, *The forsaken lover: white words and black people* (London, Routledge & Kegan Paul, 1972)
* A. Sivanandan, 'The liberation of the black intellectual' in *A different hunger* (London, Pluto, 1982)

Chapter 5
Ngugi wa Th'iongo, *Weep not child* (London, Heinemann, 1964), fiction
* Kwame Nkrumah, *Africa must unite* (London, Heinemann, 1963)
* Louis Fischer, *The life of Mahatma Gandhi* (London, Granada, 1982)

Chapter 6
Beverley Bryan et al, *The heart of the race: black women's lives in Britain* (London, Virago, 1985)
Campaign Against Racism and Fascism/Southall Rights, *Southall: the birth of a black community* (London, Institute of Race Relations, 1981)
Buchi Emecheta, *Second class citizen* (London, Allison & Busby, 1974), fiction
Ruth Glass, *Newcomers: the West Indians in London* (London, Allen & Unwin, 1960)
* Donald Hinds, *Journey to an illusion: the West Indian in Britain* (London, Heinemann, 1966)
* George Lamming, *The emigrants* (London, Allison & Busby, 1980), fiction
* Edward Scobie, *Black Brittania: a history of blacks in Britain*, part two (Chicago, Johnson Publishing Co Inc, 1972)
Samuel Selvon, *The lonely Londoners* (London, Longmans, 1980), fiction

Chapter 7
Ann Dummett, *A portrait of English racism* (London, CARAF, 1984)
* Paul Foot, *The rise of Enoch Powell* (Harmondsworth, Penguin, 1969)
Robert Moore, *Racism and black resistance in Britain* (London, Pluto, 1975)
* A. Sivanandan, *A different hunger: writings on black resistance* (London, Pluto, 1982)

Chapter 8
* Colin Brown, *Black and white Britain: the third PSI report* (London, Heinemann, 1984)
Beverley Bryan et al, *The heart of the race: black women's lives in Britain* (London, Virago, 1985)
Bernard Coard, *How the West Indian child is made educationally subnormal in the British school system* (London, New Beacon, 1971)
Campaign Against Racism and Fascism/Southall Rights, *Southall: the birth of a black community* (London, Institute of Race Relations, 1981)
Campaign Against Racism in the Media, *In black and white: racist reporting and how to fight it* (London, CARM, 1977)
Thomas J. Cottle, *Black testimony: the voices of Britain's West Indians* (London, Wildwood House, 1978)
Counter Information Services, *Racism, who profits?* (London, CIS, 1976)
Paul Gordon, *British immigration control: a brief guide* (London, Runnymede Trust, 1985)
* Paul Gordon, *White law: racism in the police, courts and prisons* (London, Pluto, 1983)
Institute of Race Relations, *Police against black people* (London, IRR, 1979)
Robert Moore, *Racism and black resistance in Britain* (London, Pluto, 1975)
* Chris Searle, *The forsaken lover: white words and black people* (London, Routledge & Kegan Paul, 1972)
* A. Sivanandan, *A different hunger: writings on black resistance* (London, Pluto, 1982)
* David J. Smith, *Racial disadvantage in Britain* (a PEP report) (Harmondsworth, Penguin, 1977)
Thames Television, *Our people* (London, Thames, 1979)
Amrit Wilson, *Finding a voice: Asian women in Britain* (London, Virago, 1978)

Chapter 9
Bethnal Green and Stepney Trades Council, *Blood on the streets* (London, Bethnal Green Trades Council, 1978)

Lorna Cocking and Hannah Charlton, *Marches, unemployment and racism* (London, ILEA, 1981)

Centre for contemporary studies, *Nazis in the playground* (London, CCS, 1981)

* David Edgar, *Destiny* (London, Methuen, 1976), a play

* Home Office, *Racial attacks: report of a Home Office study* (London, Home Office, 1981)

Tariq Mehmood, *Hand on the sun* (Harmondsworth, Penguin, 1983), fiction

Films on black resistance

Blacks Britannica, directed by David Koff and Musindo Mwinyipembe, 1978, 57 mins. Distributed by The Other Cinema.

Struggles for black community, 4 films by Race & Class Ltd, directed by Colin Prescod, 38 mins each, 1981, distributed by The Other Cinema and Concord Films:

— A common history (Leicester)
— From you you black you were out (Notting Hill)
— Tiger Bay is my home (Cardiff)
— A town under siege (Southall)